It's Easy To Play Beatles 2.

Wise Publications
London/New York/Sydney

5.95

Exclusive Distributors:
Music Sales Limited
8/9 Frith Street, London W1V 5TZ, England.
Music Sales Pty Limited
120 Rothschild Avenue, Rosebery, NSW 2018, Australia.

This book © Copyright 1990 by
Wise Publications
Order No. NO90342
ISBN 0.7119.2040.0

Art direction by Helen Senior
Cover illustration by Graham Thompson
Compiled by Peter Evans
Arranged by Daniel Scott
Music processed by Andante Computer Consultants
Typeset by Capital Setters

Music Sales' complete catalogue lists thousands of
titles and is free from your local music shop,
or direct from Music Sales Limited.
Please send £1.50 Cheque or Postal Order for postage to
Music Sales Limited, 8/9 Frith Street, London W1V 5TZ.

Printed in the United Kingdom by
Caligraving Limited, Thetford, Norfolk.

A Day In The Life

Words & Music by John Lennon & Paul McCartney

way down-stairs ____ and drank ____ a cup ____ and

look - ing up I no - ticed I was late.

Found my coat and grabbed my hat, made the

bus in sec-onds flat. Found my way up - stairs ___ and

had a smoke and some-bo-dy spoke and I went ___ in-to a dream.

2. He blew his mind out in a car,
   He didn't notice that the lights had changed.
   A crowd of people stood and stared,
   They'd seen his face before.

3. I saw a film today, oh boy,
   The English army had just won the war.
   A crowd of people turned away,
   But I just had to look.

4. I heard the news today, oh boy,
   Four thousand holes in Blackburn, Lancashire.
   And though the holes were rather small,
   They had to count them all.

Across The Universe

Words & Music by John Lennon & Paul McCartney

Words are fly-ing out like end-less rain in-to a pa-per cup, they slith-er while they pass, they slip a-way a-cross the u-ni-verse.

Pools of sor-row, waves of joy are drift-ing through my o-pened mind, pos-sess-ing and car-ess-ing me. Jai - gu - ru de

9

tum – ble blind-ly   as they make their way a –cross ___ the   un – i – verse. ___

CODA

Sounds of laugh–ter, shades of earth are   ring–ing through my o–pen views, in –   ci-ting and in–

vi – ting me. ___   Lim–it – less ___ un – dy–ing love ___ which shines a –round   me

like a mil – lion   suns, it calls me   on and on, ___ a–cross ___ the u – ni – verse. ___

Jai   –   gu – ru _____   de _____   va. ___

Get Back

Words & Music by John Lennon & Paul McCartney

Back In The USSR

Words & Music by John Lennon & Paul McCartney

Can't Buy Me Love

Words & Music by John Lennon & Paul McCartney

Every Little Thing

Words & Music by John Lennon & Paul McCartney

From Me To You

Words & Music by John Lennon & Paul McCartney

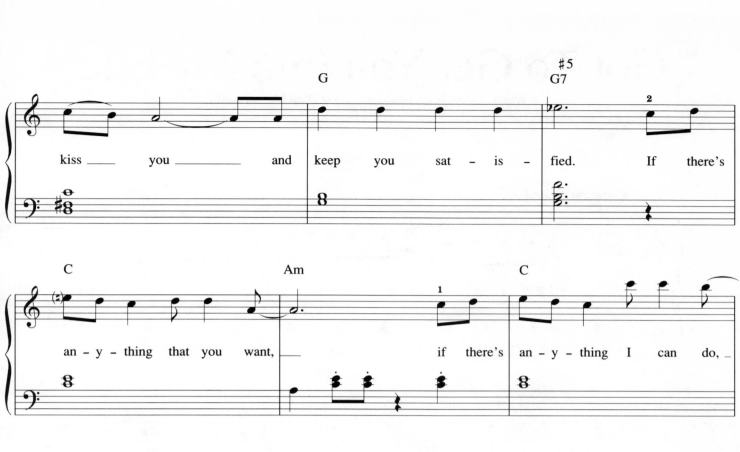

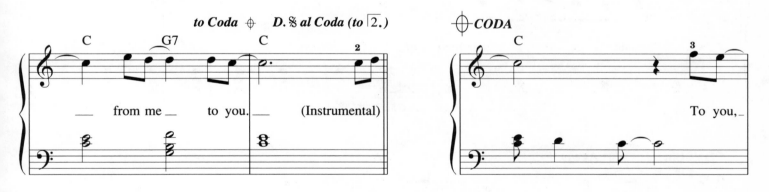

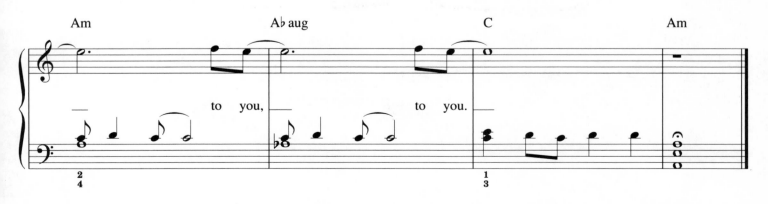

Got To Get You Into My Life

Words & Music by John Lennon & Paul McCartney

You didn't run, you didn't lie, you knew I wanted just to hold you.
And had you gone, you knew in time we'd meet again, for I had told you.
Ooh, you were meant to be near me,
Ooh, and I want you to hear me,
Say we'll be together every day.
Got to get you into my life.

What can I do, what can I be, when I'm with you I want to stay there.
If I'm true, I'll never leave and if I do I know the way there.
Ooh, then I suddenly see you,
Ooh, did I tell you I need you
Every single day of my life.
What are you doing to my life?

I Want To Hold Your Hand

Words & Music by John Lennon & Paul McCartney

Oh please, say to me, you'll let me be your man.
And please, say to me, you'll let me hold your hand.
Now let me hold your hand, I wanna hold your hand.

Yeah, you got that something, I think you'll understand.
When I feel that something, I wanna hold your hand.
I wanna hold your hand, I wanna hold your hand.

If I Fell

Words & Music by John Lennon & Paul McCartney

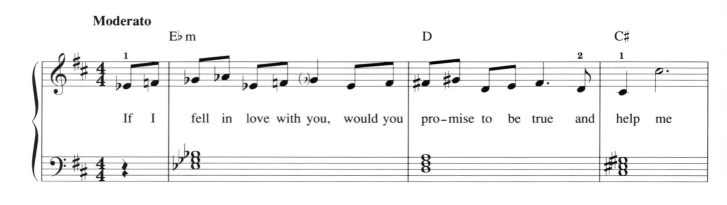

If I fell in love with you, would you pro-mise to be true and help me

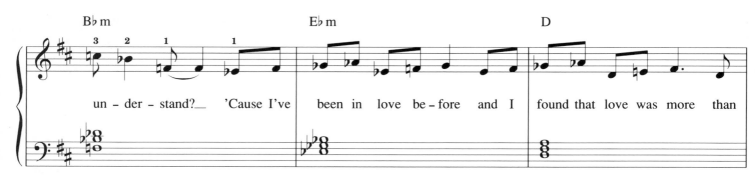

un-der-stand?__ 'Cause I've been in love be-fore and I found that love was more than

just hold-ing hands.__ If I give my heart to you, I

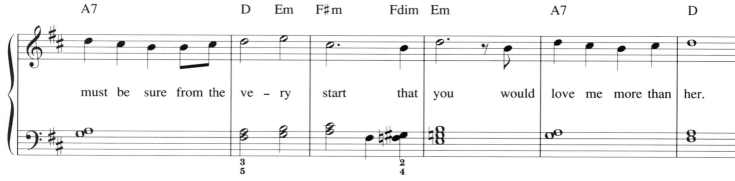

must be sure from the ve-ry start that you would love me more than her.

In My Life

Words & Music by John Lennon & Paul McCartney

But of all these friends and lovers,
There is no-one compares with you.
And these memories lose their meaning,
When I think of love as something new.
Though I know I'll never lose affection
For people and things that went before,
I know I'll often stop and think about them.
In my life, I'll love you more.

She's Leaving Home

Words & Music by John Lennon & Paul McCartney

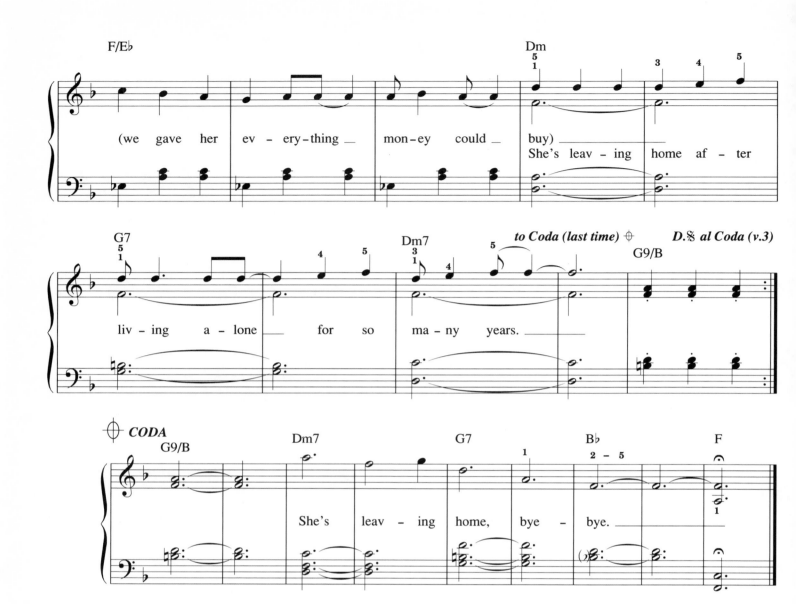

Father snores as his wife gets into her dressing gown.
Picks up the letter that's lying there,
Standing alone at the top of the stairs.
She breaks down and cries to her husband
"Daddy, our baby's gone.
Why would she treat us so thoughtlessly?
How could she do this to me?"
She (we never thought of ourselves)
is leaving (never a thought of ourselves)
Home (we struggled hard all of our lives to get by)
She's leaving home after living alone for so many years.

Friday morning at nine o' clock she is far away,
Waiting to keep an appointment she made,
Meeting a man from the motor trade.
She (what did we do that was wrong)
is leaving (we didn't know it was wrong)
Home (fun is the one thing that money can't buy)
Something inside that was always denied for so many years.
She's leaving home, bye-bye.

Lady Madonna

Words & Music by John Lennon & Paul McCartney

32

Won – der how you man – aged to feed the rest?
Lis – ten to the mu – sic playing in your head.
Won – der how you man – age to make ends meet.

33

Lucy In The Sky With Diamonds

Words & Music by John Lennon & Paul McCartney

Michelle

Words & Music by John Lennon & Paul McCartney

Ob-La-Di, Ob-La-Da

Words & Music by John Lennon & Paul McCartney

Desmond takes a trolley to the jeweller's store,
Buys a twenty carat golden ring.
Takes it back to Molly, waiting at the door
And as he gives it to her she begins to sing.
Ob-la-di, ob-la-da etc.

Happy ever after in the market-place,
Desmond lets the children lend a hand.
Molly stays at home and does her pretty face
And in the evening she still sings it with the band.
Ob-la-di, ob-la-da etc.

Paperback Writer

Words & Music by John Lennon & Paul McCartney

2. It's a dirty story of a dirty man and his clinging wife doesn't understand.
   His son is working for the Daily Mail; it's a steady job but he wants
   To be a paperback writer, paperback writer.

3. It's a thousand pages. give or take a few, I'll be writing more in a week or two.
   I can make it longer if you like the style, I can change it round
   And I want to be a paperback writer, paperback writer.

4. If you really like it, you can have the rights; I could make a million for you overnight.
   If you must return it, you can send it here, but I need a break
   And I want to be a paperback writer, a paperback writer.

She Loves You

Words & Music by John Lennon & Paul McCartney

43

Yellow Submarine

Words & Music by John Lennon & Paul McCartney

Something

Words & Music by George Harrison

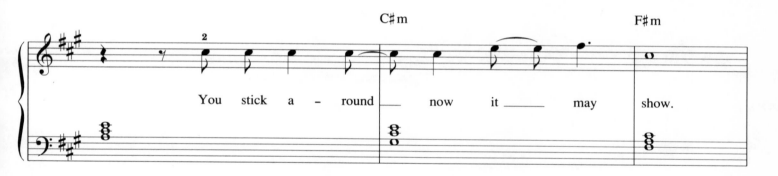

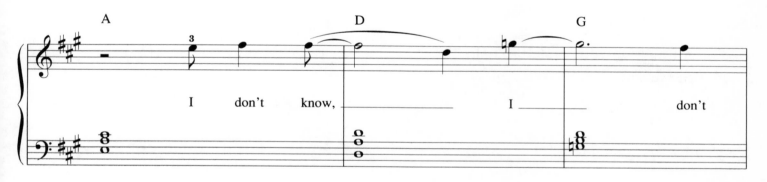

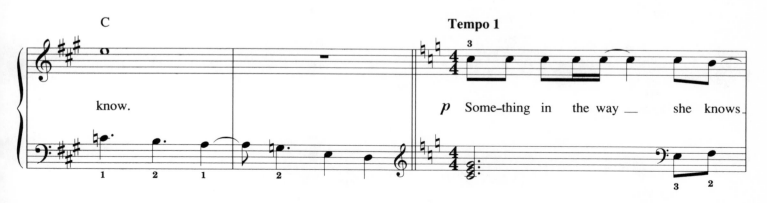